THE TALE OF THE
SHINING PRINCESS

THE TALE OF
THE SHINING
PRINCESS

ADAPTED BY Sally Fisher

FROM A TRANSLATION OF THE

STORY BY *DONALD KEENE*

The Metropolitan Museum of Art

and A Studio Book / The Viking Press

NEW YORK

The illustrations in this book are reproduced
from a late 18th-century illustrated edition
of *Taketori* ("The Bamboo Cutter"), in the
collection of The Metropolitan Museum of Art.

Rogers Fund, 1921 (21.174.1a-c)

PUBLISHED IN 1980 BY
The Metropolitan Museum of Art and
A Studio Book/The Viking Press, New York

LIBRARY OF CONGRESS CATALOGING IN PUBLICATION DATA

Fisher, Sally, 1939—
    The tale of the Shining Princess

    (A Studio book)
    "The illustrations . . . are produced directly from Taketori,
a three-volume illustrated Japanese folk tale in the collection
of the Metropolitan Museum of Art."
    SUMMARY: An extraordinarily beautiful moon princess
who is sent to Earth for punishment temporarily becomes the
daughter of a poor bamboo cutter and his wife.
    [1. Folklore—Japan] I. Keene, Donald. II. New York (City).
Metropolitan Museum of Art. III. Taketori monogatari. IV.
Title.

PZ8.1.F55Ta 1980   398.2'1'0952   80-19431
ISBN 0-87099-233-3 (MMA)
ISBN 0-670-63971-0 (VIK)

Printed in Japan

TABLE OF CONTENTS

The Shining Princess   7

The Suitors   9

The Stone Begging-bowl of the Buddha   15

The Jeweled Branch from Paradise   17

The Robe of the Fur of Chinese Fire-rats   22

The Jewel from a Dragon's Head   28

The Easy-birth Charm of the Swallows   35

The Imperial Hunt   40

The Celestial Robe of Feathers   50

Notes on the Story *by Donald Keene*   65

Notes on the Illustrations *by Andrew Pekarik*   67

THE SHINING PRINCESS

Long ago in Japan there was an old man who made his living by cutting stalks of bamboo and making clever and useful things out of them. He and his wife had a difficult and lonely life. Life was difficult because, though he worked hard, they were very poor. It was lonely because they had never had a child to bring some light and liveliness, or even something unexpected, into their days, weeks, and years.

Then late one afternoon as the forest grew dim and an early moon appeared, the bamboo cutter noticed a strange stalk of bamboo. It was glowing down near the root, as if there were a candle inside. He was mystified and leaned down to examine it. Inside the hollow bamboo was a tiny girl, no more than three inches tall! The bamboo cutter said to himself, "Since I am the only person in the world who would be here right now cutting this bamboo, I think this little child must be meant for me and my wife." He carried her home cupped in his hands, in just the way you would carry a baby bird.

The bamboo cutter and his wife were so delighted with the child that they could hardly take their eyes off her. He would hurry home from the forest in the middle of the day just to see her.

The bamboo cutter and his wife were so delighted with the child that they could hardly take their eyes off her.

Sometimes late at night his wife would rise from bed in order to look at her. Even the children from neighboring houses played in the bamboo cutter's garden, hoping for a chance to see the tiny girl. The old man made a small basket for her to sleep in, but she outgrew the basket very quickly. In fact, she grew as quickly as bamboo itself, and within three months she was fully grown!

The girl was so beautiful that she actually glowed, filling the house with warm light. If ever the old couple felt weary or pained or angry, they had only to look at her and all of their troubles would fade to nothing.

It was easy for them to raise the girl properly and give her what she needed, because something else extraordinary had begun to happen to the bamboo cutter. Often when he went out to work he would find a bamboo stalk filled with gold. Thus he gradually became a wealthy man. He was happy that he could give his daughter comfortable surroundings, pretty clothes, and servants to keep her company. Since she liked to look at pictures, he invited skilled artists to paint landscapes for their sliding doors. The once shabby house became comfortable and luxurious. But he and his wife never bothered to buy new clothes for themselves; they would have felt awkward and self-conscious in opulent robes.

When the time came to put the girl's hair up in a bun and give her a long trailing robe, she was named Nayotake no Kaguya-hime—the Shining Princess of the Young Bamboo. Her name-giving celebration continued for three days and was a wonderful feast, complete with splendid entertainments for the guests. That was when her fame began to spread, because there was clearly no woman in the world as beautiful as she.

THE SUITORS

Every man in the land was filled with desire for Kaguya-hime. Men began to gather outside her house, just to catch a glimpse of her. Some stayed for days, some for weeks, wandering outside the fence and waiting, forgetting even to eat. But finally all except the most determined gave up and went home. These were the five suitors, who vowed they would do anything to win her hand in marriage.

These five were wealthy and important men, but also celebrated lovers, the sort who would travel far to see a famous beauty. Yet in the strength of their desire for Kaguya-hime, they forgot about all other women. They wrote her letters which she did not answer. They made up songs and poems about their longing for her, but she would not listen. They sent her flowers and dishes of candy, but all to no avail. Through the blizzards of December and the terrible heat of July, they never failed to appear outside her house. Again and again, they begged the bamboo cutter to consider their plight.

For his own part, the old man was beginning to wonder whether Kaguya-hime should think about marrying: Even though she seemed an unusual creature and not of this world, he was old and worried about her future. He asked her if she would consider a suggestion he wanted to make. The girl replied that she thought of him as her father and that she would never refuse him. She promised to consent to anything he might ask.

"How happy your words make me!" he said. "It is the custom

OVERLEAF:
The suitors begged the bamboo cutter to consider their plight.

on earth for men and women to marry and have families. Why don't you marry?"

Kaguya-hime was clearly shocked. "Why in the world should I do a thing like *that*?" she asked. The old man answered, "Though you are obviously not an ordinary human being, you are still living the life of an earthly woman. While I am alive, you may choose not to marry if you wish. But I will not live forever. Some day you will be left alone. Five gentlemen have been coming here without fail for months, years in fact. Why not listen to them, and choose the one you like best to be your husband?"

The young woman tried to think of an answer. Finally she said, "Well, it would certainly be terrible if one of these men, after marrying me, turned out to be fickle. I cannot choose one of them, however grand he might be, without being absolutely sure that he is an honest man whose feelings are deep and unwavering."

"You are absolutely right," replied the bamboo cutter. "But these men have already shown remarkable faithfulness. How much more feeling can you ask them to have?"

"I do not require unusual depth of feeling," said the girl (though a moment earlier she had said just that). "They all seem to have deep enough feelings." She was silent for a moment, but then seemed to have an idea. "I propose a simple requirement. If one of them can fulfill a wish by bringing me something I desire, it will prove him the most noble and deserving. Please tell that to the gentlemen if they should come to visit again."

Of course they did come again, that very evening at sunset, their usual time to pay a call. One of them played a flute, the next recited a poem, and the rest sang from a score and whistled, keeping time by tapping their fans. In the midst of their little program, the bamboo cutter appeared.

"You have honored me and my humble household greatly by visiting month after month and year after year," he said. "I have talked with Kaguya-hime about my advancing age and suggested to her that she would do well to choose one of you as a husband. She wishes to be sure that your affections are genuine. She will choose the one who will bring her something she has always wanted. I approve of her plan, because it will prevent resentments and arguments when she has made her choice." All five men agreed happily, and the old man returned to Kaguya-hime.

Then she told her father the five tasks. "I would like to see the begging-bowl of the Buddha. That will be Prince Ishizukuri's task. Prince Kuramochi must go to Hōrai, the Mountain of Paradise in the Eastern Sea, and bring back the branch that bears fruit of white jewels from the golden tree with silver roots. From the third man, the Minister of the Right Abe no Mimuraji, I would like a robe made of the magic fur of the Chinese fire-rats, the fur that cannot be burned in fire. Ōtomo, the Grand Counselor, must bring a five-colored jewel from a dragon's head. From Isonokami, the Middle Counselor, I would like one of the magic charms from the body of a swallow, the kind of charm that ensures easy childbirth."

The old man was so astonished that for a moment he could hardly speak. "How can I go outside and tell the gentlemen what you have asked? Those things cannot be found in Japan."

Kaguya-hime turned to gaze at a painting in the room. "I don't see what's so difficult about those tasks," she said quietly.

The bamboo cutter sighed, "Anyway, I must tell them." Outside, he described the tasks as quickly and quietly as he could. The nobles said, "Why didn't she just say, 'Go away and stay away'?" They went home feeling hopeless, angry, and tricked.

THE STONE BEGGING-BOWL OF THE BUDDHA

But as time passed the suitors began to have second thoughts. Prince Ishizukuri was smart enough to know that even if he were to travel the hundred or thousand or million miles to India, he would still have almost no chance at all of finding the true begging-bowl that once belonged to the Buddha. He left word with Kaguya-hime that he was off on a trip to India. He stayed away for three years, though India was not where he went. In the province of Yamato he went to the kitchen of a mountain temple and found a pot that had hung there for many years and was black with soot. "At least it looks very ancient," he thought. He put the pot in a brocade bag and fastened the bag with some silk flowers. Then he attached a message in the form of a poem, because an

When the nobles heard their assigned tasks they felt hopeless, angry, and tricked.

15

important occasion always called for a poem in those days. Though the exact text is lost the poem said something like this:

I am worn and weary from following
the water roads of the sea
and the stone roads of the mountains.
Oceans of my tears have flowed
in the search for this bowl of stone.

When Kaguya-hime reached into the bag of brocade she removed the grimy bowl suspiciously and with a hint of distaste. She noticed immediately that it did not glow at all, that it gave off not even so much light as a firefly. She handed the bowl back to the Prince with a verse of her own.

The Buddha's bowl would have shone with the light of heaven;
this one will not sparkle with even the sun's reflection.
Surely it came from a dark, dark place.

Once outside the gate the Prince dropped the bowl on the roadside and composed a reply.

Perhaps the bowl lost its light
when it met with your glorious brightness.

Kaguya-hime chose not to answer this message, and after a few more useless pleas, the Prince left her house, staring at the ground and muttering to himself as he walked down the road.

THE JEWELED BRANCH
FROM PARADISE

Now Prince Kuramochi was a man of plans and strategies. To do things in a simple way was not in his nature. He told his court that he had not been feeling well and was going off to Tsukushi to take the cure at the hot springs. At the same time he sent word to Kaguya-hime that he was actually off on the quest for the jeweled branch, but wanted no one else to know. He was accompanied to his ship by members of the court who bade their farewells. Then after three days on the water he had the ship rowed back to a secret port.

Before leaving, the Prince had arranged for six of the world's finest jewelers to be hidden away in a specially built house in the mountains and for the house to be surrounded by three walls. There he joined them, while the tax revenues of all his sixteen domains were used to buy gold and jewels to produce a branch exactly to Kaguya-hime's specifications. The Prince lived at his ease, but he watched the jewelers' progress daily.

After three years and much exacting work, the branch was ready. The Prince notified his household that he would return by sea very soon. His message was full of hints that he was exhausted and in pain. Throngs of people went to meet the ship. The Prince had been careful to splash salt water on his clothes. He staggered ashore carrying a long wooden box in his arms and proceeded straight to the house of Kaguya-hime.

When he arrived at the gate, the Prince apologized to the bamboo cutter for his appearance and begged the old man to take the jeweled branch to his daughter. The old man told her, "The Prince has come directly here in his traveling clothes without even going home first. Open the box and see whether he has really brought the jeweled branch!" Attached to the branch was a poem that said,

> Even had I returned as a corpse,
> I'd have held this branch in my arms, for you.

The girl read this poem and stared at the beautiful branch with sorrowful eyes. "This is a terrible surprise!" she said.

Her father could not understand. "He has done everything exactly as you asked. In all Japan there is not another branch of jewels such as this. And besides, he is a very handsome man. What more could you ask?"

She answered, "It was only because I love you and could not say no to you, Father, that I asked such outrageous things of these men. It is really very upsetting that one of them should surprise me by actually performing one of those tasks."

The old man ignored her words. He invited the Prince to join them and asked, "In what kind of place did you find the tree that bore this unbelievably beautiful branch?" The Prince began, in a voice that rose and fell, in phrases now slow, now full of speed and excitement, to tell his story:

"Three years ago, on approximately the tenth day of the second moon, I boarded ship and put out to sea from the port of Naniwa. I had not the slightest idea which direction to take, but since I knew that life would not be worth living unless I could gain the object of my search, I decided to let the winds send me where they would. 'After all,' I reflected, 'if I die I will have done my utmost,

"This is a terrible surprise!" said Kaguya-hime.

18

but as long as I remain alive, I will keep sailing, just on the mere chance that I will some day come upon the mountain called Hōrai.' The ship drifted farther and farther away from Japan. Sometimes the waves were so high I was sure we would be plunged to the ocean's floor. Then sometimes we were carried by cruel winds to weird lands full of demon-like hideous beings who tried to murder us. Sometimes we lost all direction and drifted aimlessly and blindly. We had little or nothing to eat. When our food ran out we stayed alive by sucking on seashells. Then again there were times when horrible monsters rose up from the waters, intending to devour us.

"No one could help us. We were sick with every imaginable disease. But finally, at about the hour of eight o'clock in the morning on the five-hundredth day of our journey, we thought we saw a distant mountain rising from the sea. We squinted and stared, straining our eyes in its direction. Yes! It was a sublime, enormous, beautiful mountain, floating impossibly on the ocean, graceful and tall. 'This,' I thought, 'must indeed be the mountain I seek.'

"Nevertheless, I could not overcome my fear. For two or three days we sailed around the mountain. Finally I spied a woman dressed like a heavenly being, dipping water with a silver bowl. With great caution I went ashore and asked her the name of the mountain. 'This,' she replied, 'is the mountain of Hōrai.' I asked, 'With whom do I have the honor of speaking?' She answered, 'My name is Ukanruri.' And with those words, she vanished. I circled the island on foot. Flowering trees were everywhere; streams of gold, silver, and emerald gushed down the mountainside. Jeweled bridges spanned the streams. And before me stood a sparkling tree, one of many, whose branch I broke off. I chose the branch, not because it was the most glorious of all, but because it was exactly the branch described by your daughter.

"Unbelievably beautiful as the mountain island was, once I had obtained the object of my quest, I could not rest until I had returned and offered it to Kaguya-hime. The ship met with favorable winds and reached port in four hundred days. This swift return was perhaps the result of the power of my many prayers. I came directly without so much as changing my clothes, and here, as you can see, I am."

When the Prince had finished, the bamboo cutter was moved to recite a poem.

All my years of bending and cutting bamboo
had not one moment of hardship to match yours.

In turn, the Prince recited to the old man,

But now my sleeve is dry:
gone is the sea water,
gone the salt tears,
and gone the very memory of hardship.

At just that moment, six men burst through the gate. The leader unfolded a paper that looked very much like a bill, and said, "I am an artisan of the Office of Handicrafts. For over a thousand days I worked long hours making a jeweled branch under contract to the Prince who stands before you. However, I have not been paid! My assistants need their wages!" The other five joined in with a cry, "We should be paid!"

Kaguya-hime turned aside trying to conceal her smile, but she finally broke into peals of laughter. She called her father to her and whispered, "I really thought the branch came from a tree in Paradise! Give it back to him, please." And she wrote a poem in reply to the Prince.

> *A clever, attractive fake is a confusing thing;*
> *and that is what you have in common with these blossoms.*

The old bamboo cutter, sorry that he had tried so hard to convince her to marry the Prince, shut his eyes. The Prince didn't know whether to stand up or sit down. He walked around outside and snuck away when it grew dark. Kaguya-hime paid the six jewelers generously. But the Prince, who was even a worse counterfeit than the girl and her father ever knew, sent a band of thugs to rob the craftsmen on their way home.

It is said that not long afterward, the Prince went up into the mountains and disappeared. It is not known whether he did so out of true shame or just embarrassment.

THE ROBE OF THE FUR OF CHINESE FIRE-RATS

The Minister of the Right Abe no Mimuraji was a wealthy man with a great house full of servants and assistants. He was an optimistic man whose experience had been that most things can be accomplished with money, if there is enough of it. He set about immediately to arrange for the purchase of a robe of fire-rat fur. A well-known Chinese merchant named Wang Ching was just then in the port of Hakata. The Minister sent a reliable assistant named Fusamori to Wang with a large sum of gold and a letter explaining his wish to import the robe from China.

Upon reading the letter, Wang sent the following reply to the Minister: "As far as I know, there are no such things in my country as robes made of fire-rat fur. I have heard of them, naturally, but never in my life have I seen one. Though they are considered Chinese items, I suspect that if any such robe exists it is to be found in India. Therefore I will make inquiries among my Indian acquaintances of wealth and influence. Many messengers will be required and if such a robe should be found I do not doubt that purchasing it will be a complicated matter. If I am unable to obtain the robe, I will return your money in the hands of your servant."

So Wang took Fusamori on his ship. After some time the Minister learned of the ship's return. He sent a swift horse to meet Fusamori and awaited him with great excitement. As soon as Fusamori dismounted, the Minister asked about the robe. Fusamori opened a letter from Wang and read it aloud. "I am sending with your servant the famed robe of fire-rat fur, which I have obtained for you with great difficulty and at considerable expense to myself. After dispatching countless messengers to investigate the matter, I was finally informed that the robe had, in fact, come to China at some time in the very distant past. An Indian priest was said to have brought it here and the robe was believed to be in a mountain temple far to the west. I hastened to the location to verify this rumor. The robe was indeed there and, with the assistance of certain authorities, I was able to purchase it. These authorities required more money of me than the amount you supplied, so I found it necessary to add some of my own. Therefore, I request that you send fifty ounces of gold by return ship. If, however, this arrangement does not meet with your approval, you may of course return the robe. I await your prompt reply. Yours very truly, Wang Ching."

"A mere fifty ounces!" the Minister exclaimed. "How could I refuse when he has actually found and sent me the miraculous robe!" With this the Minister bowed deeply and reverently in the direction of China.

He turned then to open the gorgeous jewel-covered box that contained the robe. The fur was dark blue-gray. The tips of the hairs seemed to glow like gold. "Oh, this is too wonderful! This is clearly the robe Kaguya-hime spoke of." He almost jumped with glee, and hastened to dress himself in his best clothes, because he expected the princess to marry him that very night. He attached a branch to the box and wrote a poem for the occasion.

> For months on end I burned
> in the cruel flames of desire.
> But soothed at last, I wear
> a robe immune to fire!

At Kaguya-hime's gate, the bamboo cutter accepted the present and took it inside to show to the girl. "It is lovely!" she exclaimed. "But of course I can't tell yet whether it is genuine."

"Whether it is or not," the bamboo cutter said, "it is obviously the most beautiful robe in all Japan, and you would be wise to consider it genuine. Why do you make things so difficult? I am going to invite the Minister inside."

The old woman, hearing her husband talk this way, thought that surely this time there would be a marriage. Though the bamboo cutter did not consider it proper to force the girl to marry against her will, he had spoken quite strongly about the robe. Kaguya-hime said, "This robe is so surpassingly beautiful that everyone seems to believe it is genuine. Therefore, I know that no one will object if we test it in the fire, just to be sure." The old man sighed and replied, "Yes, I suppose that is reasonable." A fire was built in the garden. The girl and her maids watched from inside as the beautiful robe was laid in the flames. It sizzled and blazed and within a minute was burnt to a film of ashes. Kaguya-hime turned away and said brightly, "I thought so! The wrong fur."

The Minister turned the color of pale grass. The girl quickly wrote a poem and dropped it into the jeweled box.

Had I known the fur would burn in a flash,
I'd not have reduced such beauty to ash!

The Minister read the poem, picked up the box, and left without a word.

OVERLEAF:
The beautiful robe was laid in the flames.

THE JEWEL FROM A DRAGON'S HEAD

Ōtomo no Miyuki, the Grand Counselor, had a large household full of good and clever servants, clever enough never to let it be known that sometimes they found his requests ridiculous. They simply did what he said, even if it might be unwise, wasteful, or impractical. The Grand Counselor was accustomed to getting his own way.

One day he called the servants together. "I have an announcement that I know will please you," he began. "In the head of all dragons is a sparkling jewel of five colors. Whoever finds one and brings it back will be given whatever reward he wishes!"

Complete silence fell among the servants. Then one of them began carefully, "Your lordship, this is a very gracious offer, but, though the reward is most tempting, I cannot imagine that any of us could complete the task successfully, no matter how hard he might try. Jewels are not so easy to find just for the looking, let alone jewels from the heads of dragons."

The Grand Counselor appeared quite astonished. "I needn't remind you that it is the duty of servants to obey their masters even if they must risk their lives! Besides, it's not as if I were asking you even to leave your native country. Japan is full of dragons! Every day you hear of dragons rising from the sea, dragons roaming in the mountains, dragons coming down from the sky. All you need to do is locate a dragon, kill it, snatch the jewel from its

"I have an announcement that I know will please you," said the Grand Counselor.

head, and bring it here to me. Now, off you go. I'm counting on you!"

The servants realized immediately that reward or no reward, they were now under orders. They promised to find the jewel no matter what the consequences. The Grand Counselor smiled and told them that his trust in them was not misplaced. He gave them all the satins, raw silk, and copper coins in his palace so they could pay for food and other necessities as they traveled. "As a sacrifice on your behalf," he said, "we at the palace will eat no meat until your return. But don't come back until the jewel is found!"

The servants left the house quietly. Some distance away, they sat down and divided the valuables evenly among themselves. It took them only a moment to agree. "This time he has asked a truly crazy thing of us. It is not our duty to obey." They parted amiably, each one going a different way. Some went to stay with relatives they had not visited in a long time. Some traveled to places they had always wanted to see.

The Grand Counselor paced about in his palace, looking forward to his marriage to Kaguya-hime. He neglected his first wife completely. All the women in the household were made busy preparing for the new wife's arrival. The Grand Counselor had a beautiful house built for her. It was varnished with lacquer, and the walls were sprinkled with gold. As a finishing touch he ordered that the roof be thatched with silken threads dyed in all the colors of the rainbow. The workmen seemed skeptical about this idea, but remained silent as they thatched the unusual roof.

Finally the Grand Counselor grew impatient and went out in a disguise to seek some news of his servants. At the river he asked a boatman what he had heard about the servants of the Grand Counselor Ōtomo who were engaged in the famous attempt to slay a dragon and obtain the jewel from its head.

"What a story!" the boatman said. "There's no one around here doing that kind of work!"

"Just the kind of answer you'd expect from a boatman," thought the Grand Counselor. "The poor fool doesn't know what's going on." But by now his patience was almost gone. "I am a perfectly able man with a bow and arrow," he thought. "I will hire a small ship with a trusty crew and go out after a dragon myself. I can't wait for those slowpokes any longer."

The ship sailed on and on until it reached a distant ocean. There the sky grew dark and the waves began to rise, lifting the craft high in the air and dropping it as if it were a toy. The Grand Counselor became quite seasick. "What will become of us?" he shouted to the steersman. "Do something! When I boarded this ship I put my trust in you. You are the steersman. Save us! Immediately!" Just then the thunder demon began to rattle the ship with a terrifying noise. Rain tore down upon them and lightning flashed above the cabin, just missing the little vessel.

The steersman turned to the Grand Counselor. "I am a steersman, not a god. I have never seen such a terrible storm. I am certain that this is the work of dragons. You must pray to the gods at once. If we are lucky we will be washed ashore on some South Sea island."

The Grand Counselor lifted his eyes to the sky. "God of steersmen, hear me please! I have changed my plans. I promise never, never to touch so much as one hair on a dragon!" He repeated this

vow over and over, alternately standing and falling to the deck, until finally the sea was quiet and only a warm breeze moved in the sky.

"At last," said the steersman, "we are sailing in the direction of Japan." The Counselor, who lay face down on the deck, was too sick and afraid to look up and did not believe him. When they reached land, the crew had to carry the Counselor ashore. Only when they had seated him on a red robe under a pine tree did he begin to believe that he was in Japan and not on some strange island in the South Seas.

When the servants heard of their master's misadventure, they returned to him, hoping to be forgiven for failing to search for a five-colored jewel. "I'm glad you didn't try," the Counselor exclaimed. "Many of you would have been killed, and had you succeeded, I would surely have paid with my life. Thunders and dragons are in the same family and are not to be tampered with." From his remaining riches he rewarded the servants. "To think that I trusted that Kaguya-hime!" he said. "She meant to destroy us all!"

The Grand Counselor's first wife laughed about the episode until her sides hurt. The thatched roof of silk had completely vanished by then because birds had carried off the threads to line their nests. There were many beautiful birds' nests in the Grand Counselor's district that year.

The thunder demon began to rattle the ship with a terrifying noise.

The Grand Counselor began to believe that he was in Japan, not on some strange island in the South Seas.

THE EASY-BIRTH CHARM
OF THE SWALLOWS

Report all nest-building swallows to me at once!" said the Middle Counselor Isonokami no Marotari to his advisors and servants one day. They could not resist asking why. "Because I want one of the charms that help the swallows give birth to their young. It is very important that I have one," he added, though he would say no more.

The employees and advisors of the Middle Counselor exchanged glances with one another. They seemed in doubt as to what to say. One man spoke up, "I have heard this charm referred to on occasion, but I must say that I have shot down many swallows and cleaned them for cooking, and I have never found any such thing in their bellies. If you think about it, it does seem difficult to believe that a swallow could pull such a thing out of herself just before giving birth to her young."

The Middle Counselor did not seem interested in this information at all. Someone else remarked, "I've heard that the very minute a man lays eyes on one of these charms, it disappears." That did not seem to impress the Middle Counselor either. (No one could bring himself to say, "There is simply no such thing as the easy-birth charm of the swallows.")

Finally, another advisor offered a suggestion. "Well, there are swallows building nests in the holes under the eaves of the kitchen. If a number of dependable men were to sit on perches and watch, they could report to you what actually transpires when the young are born. If a charm should appear, it could be seized then."

"Fascinating!" said the Middle Counselor. "I had no idea we had all those swallows' nests right on the premises! How very exciting!" And he had perches built for twenty men. But between the twenty men and the constant stream of messengers he sent to find out what was happening, there was such commotion that the swallows took fright and escaped to the trees, where they stayed, too nervous to return to their nests at all.

An old man who worked in the kitchen was quite amused by all this activity. He said that he had a plan to suggest, and was taken to see the Counselor. "The many men are terrifying the swallows," he said in his small, feeble voice. "Take down all the perches and put one lightweight, agile man in a basket. Attach the basket to a rope so that it can be hoisted up to a nest when the swallow is about to give birth. Conceal the man and basket by covering them with a robe. Then wait for the birth signs to begin."

"What are the birth signs?" everyone asked.

"Report all nest-building swallows to me!"

36

"When a swallow is about to give birth it raises its tail and circles around. That is the time to snatch the charm."

"How greatly pleased I am to have an answer to my prayers, even if it comes from someone not in my household," said the Middle Counselor. He gave the old man a priceless robe as a reward and added, "Come back tomorrow if you would like a job in the kitchen." The old man accepted the robe and did not mention the fact that he had been working in the Counselor's kitchen for years.

At dark everything was done according to the plan, but when the man was hoisted up he said that he could feel nothing in the nest. The Middle Counselor was disgusted. "The only way to get something done properly is to do it yourself," he said. He climbed into the basket and was raised up by the creaking rope. The swallow was circling madly with its tail raised. The Counselor reached into the nest. "I have it!" he shouted. "Get me down, I have it!"

In their haste, the men below let the rope go too abruptly. It snapped, dropping the Counselor into a huge cooking pot. Though he was hurt, he held his fist tightly closed and demanded that a torch be brought so he could see the charm. He opened his hand to reveal nothing but bird-droppings.

The Middle Counselor recovered from his injury, but not from his great embarrassment. He did everything he could to keep his foolishness a secret and worried so continually about the story's spreading that he began to grow very weak. He was much more upset about the thought of people laughing at him than he was about his failure to get the charm. He became more and more ill,

The swallows took fright and escaped to the trees.

probably because he thought it would be better to die than be disgraced. Kaguya-hime heard of his troubles and sent him a little poem to cheer him up.

> I wait in the pines, patient as a tree,
> yet I hear nothing from you.
> Is it true you have no charm for me?

When he heard the poem the Counselor was overjoyed. He believed that Kaguya-hime had heard nothing about the bird-droppings, and he was flattered to the point of ecstasy by her interest in him. With great effort he composed his reply: "In despair I was ready to die, but you have saved my life." Then he died happily.

THE IMPERIAL HUNT

The failure of the five suitors to win Kaguya-hime's hand served only to increase her fame, which spread even to the palace of the Emperor. One day His Majesty said to a maid of honor, "I want you to go and see just what kind of woman this is who has meant the destruction of so many men."

When the maid of honor arrived at the bamboo cutter's house she said, "I have been sent by the Emperor to discover whether your daughter is as beautiful as people say she is." The bamboo cutter's wife bowed deeply and went quickly inside to fetch Kaguya-hime.

The girl's answer was a great shock to the old woman: "Oh, not today," she said. "I look terribly unattractive today."

"But that is ridiculous!" said her mother. "You are beautiful, as always. And surely you would not show such disrespect to a representative of the Emperor."

"If the Emperor himself were outside, it would make little difference to me," Kaguya-hime replied. Though the old woman considered Kaguya-hime her very own daughter, she had always felt a certain awe of the girl and could not scold her for this disrespectful behavior.

The maid of honor, upon hearing that the girl would not come out of the house, said, "Can it be true that anyone in the realm would disobey the Emperor's command? How can I return without having so much as glimpsed her? How will I explain my failure?" Kaguya-hime's answer was, "If I am disobeying a royal command, let me be executed."

When the Emperor heard this he said, "Indeed, I see how she could cause the ruin of many." But, not discouraged, he sent for the bamboo cutter, who hurried to the palace at once. He apologized again and again for his daughter's behavior, but explained that he had little control over what she said. The Emperor told him politely that he could not understand how a child he and his wife had raised themselves could possibly refuse to do what they desired. He offered them a position in the court, if they would bring the girl along.

It had not entered the wildest dreams of the old couple that they would ever be welcome at the Emperor's court. They could hardly believe that such an offer had been made. But when they told

OVERLEAF:
The bamboo cutter apologized again and again for his daughter's behavior.

Kaguya-hime, she replied, "If I agree to this arrangement, it will surely mean my death. You may say yes to him if you wish, but be prepared for me to die."

"We will never agree, then!" said the old man. "Court rank means nothing to us if it will endanger your life." He returned to the Emperor with his daughter's answer and explained that she was in fact not an ordinary human, but a child he had found in the mountains who had many mysterious ways. The Emperor listened and replied, "Since you live near the mountains, might I not organize an imperial hunting party as an excuse to look upon this marvelous creature?" The old man agreed to the plan and went home.

On the day of the hunt, the Emperor was dressed in a gold-embroidered robe. He came through the bamboo cutter's door as if by accident. There he saw a young woman sitting quietly, surrounded by a lovely unearthly light. She was the most beautiful being he had ever seen. He approached her slowly. As soon as Kaguya-hime noticed his presence, she rose and tried to run farther inside the house. He caught her by the sleeve. She covered her face, but it was already too late; the Emperor had lost his heart completely. "I shall not let you go," he declared.

"Were I an ordinary human I would gladly go with you," said Kaguya-hime. "But I was not born on earth. You will be unable to take me." The Emperor called to his guards for help. But though he held her sleeve tightly, Kaguya-hime suddenly and instantly vanished from sight, leaving only a pool of light where she had been.

"Now I see that you are not a mortal," he cried. "I promise to try no longer to take you with me. But please return to your human form again. Let me see you one more time before I go."

Kaguya-hime became visible again. The Emperor tried to behave in his usual manner. He rewarded the bamboo cutter generously for letting him see the princess. The bamboo cutter in turn

entertained the Emperor and all his officers with a fine banquet. Throughout the feast, the Emperor was filled with love for Kaguya-hime. Finally, as evening fell, he rose reluctantly and said good-bye. On the way back to the palace he wrote this poem and sent it to her:

> The carriage that takes the Emperor home is almost empty,
> because his soul remains at the house of Kaguya-hime.

At the palace he found that the court ladies seemed almost less than human, though in fact they were very lovely. He spent his time alone, and would sometimes write a poem for Kaguya-hime. When he found a branch or flower that was unusually beautiful, he would send it to her with a poem or letter. Her replies were by no means indifferent.

The Emperor rose reluctantly and said good-bye.

THE CELESTIAL ROBE OF FEATHERS

Thus the Emperor and Kaguya-hime wrote to one another, always kindly and with much feeling. Three years passed this way, both of them living rather lonely lives, but consoled by their friendship. One night in spring, a maidservant in the bamboo cutter's household noticed the girl sitting in the garden, looking up at the moon with tears in her eyes. "It is said that one should never look at the moon for very long," the maid reminded her. After that Kaguya-hime tried to avoid being seen when she gazed at the moon. But her father could not help noticing how often she went outside at night, especially when the moon was full, and how very pre-occupied and melancholy she seemed. He became more and more worried about her, and finally asked, "My dear, what are you thinking about? What is upsetting you?"

"It is nothing, except that the world seems such a sad and lonely place," she answered. The old man begged her to stop looking at the moon, but she replied that she could not. "How could I live if I could not see the moon? The whole world is so dreary to me."

Finally, one summer night her father noticed Kaguya-hime sitting in the moonlight weeping bitterly, too unhappy to care whether or not she was seen. He begged her to explain the cause of her sorrow.

"I have known something for a long time now, but could not bring myself to tell you," she replied. "I so hate the thought of upsetting you. But now the time has come for me to speak. I have no choice but to explain everything.

"I am not from the earth but from the Palace of the Moon. I was sent here because of something I did long ago. I never meant to stay this long, but I became so fond of you that I could not leave. I have a mother and father in the Palace of the Moon, though I have not thought of them while here on earth. I do not look forward to my return. I feel only a terrible sadness at the thought of leaving you, yet very soon I must go. My people will come to take me home."

Kaguya-hime and her parents wept uncontrollably. The servants of the house came to them and heard the sad news. They too fell to weeping. None of them could imagine living without the maiden's luminous beauty and exquisite manners. All of the household was lost in grief.

It did not take long for this unhappy news to reach the Imperial

OVERLEAF:
"I have no choice but to explain everything," Kaguya-hime said.

Palace. A messenger from the Emperor came to the old man within a few days' time. The bamboo cutter seemed to have grown much older and his eyes were swollen with weeping. He asked the messenger whether the Emperor would send soldiers to fend off the moon men and save his daughter. On hearing the request the Emperor answered, "If I, who saw her only once, cannot keep her from my thoughts, I can only imagine what losing her would mean to those who have lived with her for days, weeks, and years."

On the day of the full moon the Emperor sent two thousand soldiers to the bamboo cutter's house. Their bodies were protected with woven armor. They stationed themselves on the walls and roof, made ready their bows and arrows, and began to watch the sky anxiously. The women guarded the inside of the house. In the innermost room, Kaguya-hime's mother held the girl in her arms. The old man locked the door and stood guard. "Do not take your eyes from the sky," he ordered the soldiers.

"Not so much as a bat will escape our notice!" they answered, reassuring the old man. "Not even a mosquito!"

The strength of the Emperor's forces gave the bamboo cutter courage, and his courage fired his wrath. "I will tear them to pieces!" he shouted. "I will grab them by the hair and throw them to the ground. I will pull off their clothes and shame them in front of the Emperor's officers!"

Kaguya-hime tried to quiet him. "Please! Do not let the men on the roof hear you talk that way. Try to understand. You will not be able to resist their force. There is nothing we can do. How it hurts me to leave you this way, seeming to be so heartless. When

The bamboo cutter asked if the Emperor would send soldiers to fend off the moon men.

I went out at night to gaze at the moon, I was begging for just one more year on earth. My request was not granted; that is why I wept night after night. I wish I could stay and help you as you grow old and unable to care for yourself. People on the moon never grow old. They are very beautiful. They have no worries; their life is without care. Yet I would rather stay here on earth because I have come to love you."

The old man cried, "I don't care how beautiful they are! I shall never let those moon people daunt me!"

By now it was almost midnight. Suddenly a blazing light filled the house and garden. It was brighter than noon. White light illuminated every leaf and blade of grass. Down from the sky came men of indescribable beauty, riding on white clouds that descended around the house. The soldiers were enfeebled with fright. Their fear was so great they could barely move. They tried at last to lift their bows, but the strength had drained from their arms and hands. The bravest men tried to shoot, but their arrows fell in all directions to the ground. In their fear and astonishment they could only stare at the sight before them.

The moon men were dressed in clothing of glorious richness. With them was a chariot covered with veils of gauzy silk. The one who seemed to be their king called out, "Princess! Come! It is time."

The old man, for all his fierce threats a few moments earlier, could do nothing but fall to the ground before the ruler of the moon. He seemed to be caught in a trance.

The King continued in a lowered voice: "Old man, because you performed some good deeds when you were poor, we sent you the

The soldiers stationed themselves on the walls and roof and began to watch the sky anxiously.

princess for a short while as your reward. We have been a great help to you. Now you are a wealthy man, almost a different person.

"The princess, however, was sent for quite another reason. She was obliged to pay for a wrongdoing committed in our realm. The time for her punishment is over and she must return. However much you grieve and protest, you may have her no longer. Bring her to me at once."

The old man rallied some of his courage. In an unsteady voice he said, "Sir, your reference to 'a short while' makes me think you must have the wrong Kaguya-hime. Our Kaguya-hime has been here for a long time. Besides, she is quite unwell. I think it would be unwise to move a girl who is so seriously ill."

The King gave no answer at all to these words. He guided the floating chariot to the roof and again cried out, "Kaguya-hime, why do you linger so long in this dirty place?"

The door of the innermost room flew open of its own accord. The lattice-work shutters too broke open as if a gust of wind had blown from within the house. Kaguya-hime stepped outside and stood before the bamboo cutter who lay weeping in bewilderment.

"Please stand up, my dear father," she said. "I do not leave you of my own choosing. At least watch me as I ascend into the sky."

"How can I watch a sight so painful? Do not abandon us. Please take us with you!"

Kaguya-hime could not think what to do. "I will write you a letter," she said. "That way, whenever you miss me you can read it and be comforted." She sat and wrote, a tear falling from her eyes for each drop of ink from the brush. In the letter she told of her

A tear fell from her eyes for each drop of ink from the brush.

love for her earthly parents. She explained that had she been born in this world, she would never have caused them any unhappiness. She asked them to think of her when they looked at the moon, and to try to believe that she was returning to them each time the moon returned.

The immortals from the Moon Palace carried a jar of elixir and a robe of feathers. One of them offered the jar to Kaguya-hime. "Take some of the elixir of immortality," he said. "Your health must be poor from the things you have had to eat in this unclean place." She tasted the elixir. Then she asked for paper to write another letter. The immortals urged her to put on the celestial robe of feathers and go with them.

"Not yet," she replied. "I will lose my earthly emotions when I put on the robe, and there is someone else to whom I must say good-bye." The moon people were becoming impatient.

"It is late!" they told her.

Kaguya-hime glanced sternly at the immortals. "Do not let these people see your lack of understanding of human feelings," she replied. Very calmly she sat down again to write a letter to the Emperor.

The letter said, "I am giving to you some of the elixir of immortality. You kindly sent your valiant soldiers to defend me, but they met with forces that no earthly army could withstand. I have caused you much trouble and pain, and behaved in a way that must have been incomprehensible to you. I could not do otherwise. I leave now, though it is against my will. Until the moment I put on the celestial robe of forgetfulness, I think of you longingly as my lord."

As soon as she had finished the letter she bade farewell one more time to the bamboo cutter and his wife. Then Kaguya-hime drew the robe of feathers over her shoulders and, in that instant, all sorrow and pity left her; she could not remember what unhappiness was like. Thus she rejoined the immortals, whose experience of beauty is without the pain that accompanies all the beautiful things on earth. She stepped into the chariot and, surrounded by countless heavenly beings, rose up into the sky. A moment later, the garden was dark again. The crickets slowly resumed their singing. Only the billowing curtains gave proof of the astonishing departure.

When the Emperor received Kaguya-hime's letter, he rose and left the assembled courtiers. Seated behind a bamboo blind he read her parting words. He was distraught with unhappiness. He decided that the elixir of immortality was of little use to him since, no matter how long he might live, he could never hope to see Kaguya-hime again. He wrote a poem for her saying farewell and pledging his love, but no one has read that poem because the Emperor asked a messenger to take both it and the elixir to the top of the mountain closest to Heaven, Mount Fuji, and set fire to both. Even now, it is said that smoke is rising into the sky from the burning elixir and the Emperor's poem for the moon princess.

As for the bamboo cutter and his wife, they felt that they had little reason to live now that Kaguya-hime had left them, and in truth they did not live much longer. But it is true also that their lives had been changed completely by the presence of Kaguya-hime, the moon princess. They were no longer poor after she came to them, of course, but far more important than that, they had truly had a loving child of their own who had brought light and life and awesome beauty into their days, weeks, and years. And, they had seen and learned more about the immortals than most earth people can even guess.

Seated behind a bamboo blind, the Emperor read Kaguya-hime's parting words.

NOTES ON THE STORY

by Donald Keene

The Tale of the Shining Princess, also frequently known as *The Tale of the Bamboo Cutter*, was written about 900 A.D. We do not know who the author was. Indeed, there is reason to believe that the story was written not by one person but by several people, over a period of perhaps fifty years, before it reached its present state. The story was well known in Japan as long as a thousand years ago, as is indicated by the many references to it in later Japanese literature. For example, in *The Tale of Genji*, a long novel composed at the beginning of the eleventh century, one character says about *The Tale of the Shining Princess*, "The story has been with us a very long time, and is as familiar as the bamboo growing before us." Many people at the Japanese court read the manuscripts of the book, and probably even people in the country who could not read were familiar with the plot, having heard storytellers' accounts of the beautiful princess who came down to earth from the moon.

The central figure of the story is Kaguya-hime, who is discovered as a tiny child inside a stalk of bamboo and grows up to become the most beautiful woman in the land. She has many suitors, and some of the most exciting parts of this story are those which describe the tasks they must undertake in order to prove worthy of marrying her. Stories about suitors who must submit to such tests are found both in folklore and in world literature. In Shakespeare's play *The Merchant of Venice*, for example, each man desirous of winning the hand of the rich heiress, Portia, must choose among three caskets, one of gold, one of silver, and one of lead, the one that contains her portrait. In the story of the cruel Princess Turandot, the Princess asks three riddles of her suitors, and those men who cannot answer all three correctly not only fail to win her hand in marriage, but also have their heads cut off.

The number of tests to which suitors must submit in such stories is usually three. Originally, in *The Tale of the Shining Princess*, there were probably only three suitors rather than five. People may have found the story so interesting that two more were added to the original three. Three is an important number in the story in other ways: Kaguya-hime is three inches tall when the bamboo cutter finds her; it takes three months for her to reach her full height; and the feast held after she receives her new name lasts three days.

The tasks which the suitors are required to perform are all impossibly difficult. Kaguya-hime obviously does not want to marry anyone, and she hopes that all five suitors will fail. However, two of the suitors return with presents that seem to be exactly what she has asked for. Kaguya-hime is dismayed for she fears that she will have to submit to marriage, but fortunately for her, she discovers that both the treasures brought before her are mere imitations. Realizing that the men have deliberately tried to deceive her, she feels no pity for them when she turns them away. She does, however, feel sorry for the fifth suitor, who dies after having actually attempted to obtain for her the swallows' charm.

After the five suitors have been dismissed, the Emperor himself seeks her hand. Kaguya-hime cannot very well refuse him. Instead, she turns herself into a ball of light to demonstrate that she is no ordinary mortal. The Emperor sadly resigns himself to the fact that, despite his temporal powers, he can have no control over somebody from another world.

Finally the time comes when Kaguya-hime must return to the moon. She dons a magic robe of feathers and rises into the sky, much like a bird. The transformation of a woman into a bird is a frequent theme in folk tales all over the world. The robe of feathers makes Kaguya-hime forget her love for the bamboo cutter and his wife, and she calmly departs with her escorts, leaving not only her foster parents but also the Emperor to mourn her departure.

The story of Kaguya-hime is still widely known in Japan. Children are introduced to her in picture books, high school and college students read the original story, and people who enjoy music attend operas based on her adventures. She has also inspired many paintings, including the lovely ones in this book.

NOTES ON THE ILLUSTRATIONS

by Andrew Pekarik

The illustrations for this book are taken from a manuscript of *The Tale of the Shining Princess* that was copied in Japan near the end of the eighteenth century and belongs to The Metropolitan Museum of Art. The calligrapher probably copied the words from an older book with pictures. He knew exactly which sentences he wanted to be followed by a picture: when he came near the end of one of these sentences he would stretch it across the rest of the page, leaving the next page or two blank for the illustration. Half the paper on which he wrote his text was plain tan-colored paper, and between each of these sheets was paper painted with pale gold designs of plants, leaves, or wheels in water. The motif of the wheels in water was first used when Japanese noblemen rode in large carriages pulled by oxen. The wooden wheels of the carriages were left periodically to soak in water so their joints would remain tight.

Most modern scholars believe *The Tale of the Shining Princess* was first written between the middle of the ninth and middle of the tenth centuries. Since this was nearly one thousand years before these pictures were drawn, the artist was depicting a world very different from his own. About the year 900 the emperor of Japan was quite powerful; the most important people in the country were those in his court. As shown in the illustrations, they wore voluminous, many-layered robes; the ladies, especially, seem to emerge from mounds of beautiful fabrics. The bamboo cutter and his wife, because they are simple people, wear more practical clothes. The men of the court wore tall hats to accommodate the traditional hairdo, a stiff upward-pointing shaft of hair. In the last picture (p. 62), which shows the Emperor's court, the men wear a more formal kind of hat, with a piece of gauze hanging down, and hold in their hands the batons that were also part of formal dress.

In this scene the men are seated on a floor covered with thick mats made of fresh, green rice straw, the same kind of mats the Japanese use today. The edges are bound with cloth tape that has a design of dots and X's. At the upper left there is a particularly thick mat with a fancy border which is raised higher than the other mats. The Emperor is seated on this mat, but he is behind a bamboo blind, not visible to the viewer. Japanese artists often avoided showing the emperor's face. This tradition may have begun because artists believed that no matter how well they painted, they would not be able to do justice to the emperor's splendid appearance. Whereas a Western artist would have made the Emperor the center of attention, Japanese artists have always preferred to encourage viewers to use their imaginations.

A Western artist similarly would have focused on the climactic scene in which Kaguya-hime is carried away by the moon people. This book is special precisely because there is no picture of that most exciting moment. The Japanese artist knew that however well he might draw the moon people they would always be less interesting than those imagined by the reader.

There are, however, three pictures in which the artist did break with this tradition and illustrated unusual subjects. In two of them the Emperor is shown meeting with Kaguya-hime. He is fully visible as he visits her in her home. The artist probably felt that it was important to show directly how these two principal characters felt about each other. In the first picture where the Emperor and Kaguya-hime appear together (pp. 46–47), Kaguya-hime, holding a fan, leans toward the Emperor, who in turn leans back toward her. The old bamboo cutter and his wife watch together with several of the princess' maids. The feeling between the Emperor and Kaguya-hime is so strong that even the Emperor's servants take notice as they wait for him in the garden. (They carry tall umbrellas with white covers with which to protect the Emperor in case it should rain.) In the following picture the Emperor reluctantly leaves an unhappy Kaguya-hime, joining his servants who wait for him by his carriage. In the third unusual picture (p. 32), the artist has depicted the powerful thunder demon creating a storm. Around him circle flying drums that he strikes to sound the thunder.

This demon appears through a gap in gold-speckled clouds. These clouds are a convention of Japanese painting. They appear at the top and bottom of every picture in this book, even when there is no storm. Japan has a damp climate, and mist is frequent in the mountains. Artists probably drew bands of mist in order to cover the less interesting background details and focus attention on the important events at the center of the painting. These bands of mist later took the form of clouds, such as are illustrated in these paintings. Of course the cloud bands here don't really look like clouds because they are sprinkled with flakes of cut gold foil; the artist wanted to make pictures that looked expensive as well as pretty. He used many colors that he ground from colored rocks. He painted details on clothing with gold. He even used silver to draw the lines of water in the blue streams.

Another convention of Japanese painting was to remove the roofs of houses, entirely or in part, so that the viewer can see what is going on inside. Japanese houses were built so that they were open to the outside and flexible in design; instead of using solid, immovable walls as we have in the West, the Japanese preferred to divide their homes by the use of sliding doors covered with paper. These paper doors were suitable to paint on, and many of them were decorated with landscape scenes. The sliding doors inside the bamboo cutter's house have ink paintings of mountains on them.

The Metropolitan Museum book from which these illustrations come was probably made about 1800 for the Tokugawa family, the most powerful Samurai in Japan. At that time the Japanese emperor no longer had any power, and the country was ruled by this family. Important lords like the Tokugawas regularly employed painters and calligraphers to decorate their homes and make works of art for their families. The Museum's book is divided into three thin volumes, each with a pale blue silk cover. To hold these volumes the lord who commissioned the book ordered a gold-decorated lacquer box. The box shows bamboo shoots with leaves, birds, the family crest—three heart-shaped leaves in a circle—and at the center, the title of the book. The lid of the box has been reproduced on the cover of this book. The original decoration was made by sprinkling fine gold dust over a design drawn in wet lacquer. The birds were sprinkled with silver dust. The young lady born in a Tokugawa family who received this book would also have received many other books, all in beautiful lacquer boxes. She would have been given fancy, gold-decorated lacquer stands on which to display them and matching writing boxes she could use for practicing calligraphy and writing poetry, in much the same way that Kaguya-hime does in the next-to-last illustration.

The original album open to show
illustration and calligraphy

TRANSLATION OF JAPANESE CALLIGRAPHY

Because of this
he is full of sorrow
his hair has turned white
his back is bent
his eyes are swollen

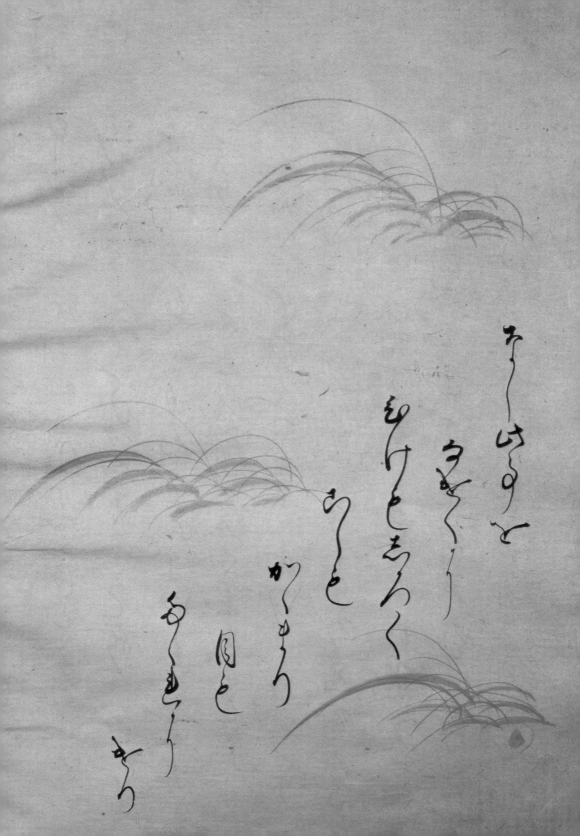

あしはらと
ゆめくり
もけもなろく
らと
かくもり
月を
あくまなり
より

Produced at The Metropolitan Museum of Art by the
Department of Special Publications; Robie Rogge,
Manager. Designed by Peter Oldenburg. Production
supervised by Osa Brown. Photographed by Walter
Yee/The Metropolitan Museum Photograph Studio.
Composition by Finn Typographic Service, Inc., Stamford,
Connecticut. Printed in seven-color offset and bound
by Toppan Printing Company, Inc., Tokyo, Japan.